SONGS OF SCOTLAND

INTRODUCTION

For a small country Scotland has a rich store of wonderful national songs. In the following pages we offer a selection of great favourites such as Song of the Clyde, Bonnie Banks of Loch Lomond, Scotland the Brave, Bonnie Wee Jeannie McColl, Donald Where's Yoor Troosers? Dancing in Kyle, Skye Boat Song, The Road to the Isles and dozens more.

To bring you all the songs of Scotland would take many volumes but we hope that you will find the following selection as being representative of the humour, heroism and romance which are to be found in our nation's store of music and lyrics.

The editors wish to thank the music companies who kindly granted permission for the use of copyright material.

Published by Lang Syne Publishers Ltd
45 Finnieston St., Glasgow
Tel: 041-204 3104
Printed by Dave Barr Print
45 Finnieston Street, Glasgow
Tel: 041-221 2598

These songs are featured on the following pages…

Ae Fond Kiss

Ae fond kiss and then we sever;
Ae fareweel, alas, for ever!
Deep in heart-wrung tears I'll pledge thee,
Warring sighs and groans I'll wage thee.
Who shall say that fortune grieves him,
While the star of hope she leaves him?
Me, nae cheerfu' twinkle lights me;
Dark despair around benights me.

I'll ne'er blame my partial fancy,
Naething could resist my Nancy:
But to see her, was to love her;
Love but her, and love for ever—
Had we never lov'd sae kindly,
Had we never lov'd sae blindly,
Never met—or never parted,
We had ne'er been broken-hearted.

Fare thee weel, thou first and fairest!
Fare thee weel, thou best and dearest!
Thine be ilka joy and treasure,
Peace, enjoyment, love and pleasure!
Ae fond kiss, and then we sever;
Ae fareweel, alas! for ever!
Deep in heart-wrung tears I pledge thee,
Warring sighs and groans I'll wage thee.

Words by Robert Burns

A Man's a Man for A'that

Is there for honest poverty
    That hangs his head, an' a' that?
The coward slave we pass him by,
We daur be puir for a' that,
For a' that, and a' that,
Our toils obscure, and a' that;
The rank is but the guinea's stamp,
The man's the gowd for a' that.

What though on hamely fare we dine,
    Wear hoddin-grey and a' that,
Gie fools their silks, and knaves their wine;
    A man's a man for a' that.
For a' that and a' that,
    Their tinsel show and a' that,
The honest man, though ne'er sae puir,
    Is king o' men for a' that.

A king can mak' a belted knight,
    A marquis, duke, and a' that;
But an honest man's aboon his micht,
    Gude faith, he maunna fa' that!
For a' that, and a' that,
    Their dignities and a' that,
The pith o' sense, and pride o' worth,
    Are higher ranks than a' that.

Then let us pray that come it may,
    As come it will, for a' that,
That sense and worth, o'er a' the earth,
    May bear the gree, and a' that.
For a' that, and a' that,
    It's comin' yet, for a' that,
When man to man, the warld o'er,
    Shall brithers be for a' that.

Words by Robert Burns

Annie Laurie

Maxwelltoun braes are bonnie, where early fa's the dew,
And 'twas there that Annie Laurie gie'd me her promise true,
Gie'd me her promise true, which ne'er forgot will be;
And for bonnie Annie Laurie I'd lay me doon and dee.

Her brow is like the snaw drift, her neck is like the swan,
And her face it is the fairest that e'er the sun shone on;
That e'er the sun shone on; and dark blue is her e'e;
And for bonnie Annie Laurie I'd lay me doon and dee.

Like dew on the gowan lying is the fa' o' her fairy feet,
And, like winds in summer sighing, her voice is low and sweet;
Her voice is low and sweet; she's a' the world to me,
And for bonnie Annie Laurie I'd lay me doon and dee.

Auld Lang Syne

Should auld acquaintance be forgot
  And never brought to mind?
Should auld acquaintance be forgot,
  And auld lang syne?

Chorus
For auld lang syne, my dear,
  For auld lang syne,
We'll tak' a cup o' kindness yet,
  For auld lang syne.

And surely ye'll be your pint-stoup,
  And surely I'll be mine;
And we'll tak' a cup o' kindness yet,
  For auld lang syne.
                    For auld, &c.

We twa hae run about the braes,
  And pou'd the gowans fine;
But we've wandered mony a weary fit,
  Sin' auld lang syne.
                    For auld, &c.

We twa hae paidl'd in the burn,
  Frae morning sun till dine;
But seas between us braid har roar'd,
  Sin' auld lang syne.
                    For auld, &c.

And there's a hand, my trusty fiere!
  And gie's a hand o'thine!
And we'll tak' a right gude-willie waught,
  For auld lang syne.
                    For auld, &c.

Words by Robert Burns

Annie Laurie

Maxwelltoun braes are bonnie, where early fa's the dew,
And 'twas there that Annie Laurie gie'd me her promise true,
Gie'd me her promise true, which ne'er forgot will be;
And for bonnie Annie Laurie I'd lay me doon and dee.

Her brow is like the snaw drift, her neck is like the swan,
And her face it is the fairest that e'er the sun shone on;
That e'er the sun shone on; and dark blue is her e'e;
And for bonnie Annie Laurie I'd lay me doon and dee.

Like dew on the gowan lying is the fa' o' her fairy feet,
And, like winds in summer sighing, her voice is low and sweet;
Her voice is low and sweet; she's a' the world to me,
And for bonnie Annie Laurie I'd lay me doon and dee.

Auld Lang Syne

Should auld acquaintance be forgot
 And never brought to mind?
Should auld acquaintance be forgot,
 And auld lang syne?

Chorus
For auld lang syne, my dear,
 For auld lang syne,
We'll tak' a cup o' kindness yet,
 For auld lang syne.

And surely ye'll be your pint-stoup,
 And surely I'll be mine;
And we'll tak' a cup o' kindness yet,
 For auld lang syne.
                              For auld, &c.

We twa hae run about the braes,
 And pou'd the gowans fine;
But we've wandered mony a weary fit,
 Sin' auld lang syne.
                              For auld, &c.

We twa hae paidl'd in the burn,
 Frae morning sun till dine;
But seas between us braid har roar'd,
 Sin' auld lang syne.
                              For auld, &c.

And there's a hand, my trusty fiere!
 And gie's a hand o'thine!
And we'll tak' a right gude-willie waught,
 For auld lang syne.
                              For auld, &c.

Words by Robert Burns

The Banks o' Doon

Ye banks and braes o' bonnie Doon,
  How can ye bloom sae fresh and fair!
How can ye chant, ye little birds,
  And I sae weary fu' o' care!

Thou'll break my heart thou warbling bird,
  That wantons thro' the flowering thorn;
Thou minds me o' departed joys,
  Departed never to return.

Oft hae I rov'd by bonnie Doon,
  To see the rose and woodbine twine;
And ilka bird sang o' its luve,
  And fondly sae did I o' mine.

Wi' lightsome heart I pu'd a rose,
  Fu' sweet upon its thorny tree;
And my fause luver staw my rose,
  But ah! he left the thorn wi' me.

Words by Robert Burns

The Birks of Aberfeldy

Bonnie Lassie, will ye go,
Will ye go, will ye go,
Bonnie Lassie, will ye go,
To the birks of Aberfeldy?

Now simmer blinks on flow'ry braes,
And o'er the crystal streamlet plays;
Come let us spend the lightsome days,
In the birks of Aberfeldy.

While o'er their heads the hazels hing,
The little birdies blithely sing,
Or lightly flit on wanton wing,
In the birks of Aberfeldy.

The braes ascend like lofty wa's,
The foamin' stream deep roaring fa's,
O'erhung wi' fragrant spreadin' shaws,
The birks of Aberfeldy.

The hoary cliffs are crown'd wi flow'rs,
White o'er the linns the burnie pours,
And risin' weets wi' misty showers,
The birks of Aberfeldy.

Let fortune's gifts at random flee,
They ne'er shall draw a wish frae me,
Supremely blest wi' love and thee,
In the birks of Aberfeldy.

Bonnie Lassie &c after each verse

Words by Robert Burns

Blue Bonnets over the Border

March! March! Ettrick and Teviotdale,
Why, the deil, dinna ye march forward in order?
March! March! Eskdale and Liddesdale,
All the Blue Bonnets are over the Border.

Many a banner spread flutters above your head,
Many a crest that is famous in story;
Mount and make ready then, sons of the mountain glen,
Fight for your king and the old Scottish glory.
                March! March! &c.

Come from the hills where your hirsels are grazing,
Come from the glen of the buck and the roe;
Come to the crag where the beacon is blazing,
Come with the buckler, the lance and the bow.
                March! March! &c.

Trumpets are sounding, warsteeds are bounding,
Stand to your arms, and march in good order:
England shall many a day tell of the bloody fray,
When the Blue Bonnets came over the Border!
                March! March! &c.

Words by Sir Walter Scott

Bonnie Banks of Loch Lomond

By yon bonnie banks and by yon bonnie braes,
Where the sun shines bright on Loch Lomond
Where me and my true love were ever wont to gae,
On the bonnie, bonnie banks o' Loch Lomond.

Chorus
O ye'll tak' the high road and I'll tak' the low road,
And I'll be in Scotland afore ye.
But me and my true love will never meet again,
On the bonnie, bonnie banks o' Loch Lomond.

'Twas there that we parted in yon shady glen,
On the steep, steep side o' Ben Lomond.
Where in deep purple hue, the hieland hills we view,
And the moon comin' out in the gloamin'.

The wee birdies sing and the wild flowers spring,
And in sunshine the waters are sleeping:
But the broken heart it kens nae second spring again,
Tho' the waefu' may cease from their greeting.

Author not known

Bonnie Dundee

To the Lords of Convention 'twas Claverhouse spoke:
"Ere the King's crown go down there are crowns to be broke,
Then each cavalier who loves honour and me,
Let him follow the bonnets of Bonnie Dundee."

Come fill up my cup, come fill up my can,
Come saddle my horses, and call out my men;
Unhook the west port, and let us gae free,
For it's up wi' the bonnets of Bonnie Dundee.

Dundee he is mounted, he rides up the street,
The bells they ring backward, the drums they are beat,
But the provost (douce man) said, "Just e'en let it be,
For the toun is weel rid o' that de'il o' Dundee."
                    Come fill up my cup &c

There are hills beyond Pentland, and lands beyond Forth,
Be there lords in the south, there are chiefs in the north;
There are brave Duinnewassels three thousand times three,
Will cry "Hey for the bonnets o' Bonnie Dundee."
                    Come fill up my cup &c

Then awa' to the hills, to the lea, to the rocks,
Ere I own a usurper I'll crouch with the fox,
And tremble, false Whigs, in the midst o' your glee,
Ye hae no seen the last o' my bonnets and me.
                    Come fill up my cup &c.

Words by Sir Walter Scott

Bonnie Wee Jeannie McColl

A fine wee lass, a bonnie wee lass, is bonnie wee Jeannie McColl,
I gave her ma mither's engagement ring and a bonnie wee tartan shawl.
I met her at a waddin' in the Co-operative Hall,
I wis the best man and she wis the belle o' the ball.

The very night I met her she wis awfy, awfy shy,
The rain cam' pourin' doon, but she was happy, so wis I;
We ran like mad fur shelter, an' we landed up a stair,
The rain cam' pourin' oot o' ma breeks, but, och, I didna care.
        For she's a &c.

Noo I've wad ma Jeannie an bairnies we hiv three,
Twa dochters and a wee, wee fellah that sits upon ma knee.
They're richt wee holy terrors an' they're never still for lang,
But they sit and listen every nicht while I sing this sang.
        Oh, she's a &c.

**Printed and published by kind permission of James S. Kerr,
Music Publishers.**

Bonnie Strathyre

There's meadows in Lanark and
  mountains in Skye,
And pastures in Hielands and Lawlands
  forbye;
But there's nae greater luck that the heart
  could desire
Than to herd the fine cattle in bonnie
  Strathyre.

O it's up in the morn and awa' to the hill,
When the lang simmer days are sae warm
  and sae still,
Till the peak o' Ben Vorlich is girdled wi' fire,
And the evenin' fa's gently on bonnie
  Strathyre.

Then there's mirth in the sheiling and love
  in my breast,
When the sun is gane doun and the kye are
  at rest;
For there's mony a prince wad be proud to
  aspire
To my winsome wee Maggie, the pride o'
  Strathyre.

Her lips are like rowans in ripe simmer seen,
And mild as the starlicht the glint o' her
  e'en
Far sweeter her breath than the scent o'
  the briar,
And her voice is sweet music in bonnie
  Strathyre.

Set Flora by Colin and Maggie by me,
And we'll dance to the pipes swellin' loudly
and free,
Till the moon in the heavens climbing higher
and higher
Bids us sleep on fresh brackens in bonnie
Strathyre.

Though some to gay touns in the Lawlands
will roam,
And some will gang sodgerin' far from their
home;
Yet I'll aye herd my cattle, and bigg my ain byre,
And love my ain Maggie in bonnie Strathyre.

**Published by kind permission of J.B. Cramer
and Co. Ltd.**

The Campbells are Comin'

The Campbells are comin', O-ho, O-ho,
The Campbells are comin'. O-ho. O-ho.
The Campbells are comin' to bonnie Lochleven,
The Campbells are comin', O-ho, O-ho.
Upon the Lomonds I lay, I lay,
Upon the Lomonds I lay, I lay,
I looked down to bonnie Lochleven,
And saw three bonnie pipers play.

The Campbells are comin', O-ho, O-ho,
The Campbells are comin', O-ho, O-ho,
The Campbells are comin' to bonnie Lochleven,
The Campbells are comin' O-ho, O-ho.
The great Argyle he goes before,
He makes the cannons and guns to roar;
Wi' sound o' trumpet, pipe and drum,
The Campbells are comin', O-ho, O-ho.

The Campbells are comin', O-ho, O-ho,
The Campbells are comin', O-ho, O-ho,
The Campbells are comin' to bonnie Lochleven,
The Campbells are comin', O-ho, O-ho.
The Campbells they are a' in arms,
Their loyal faith and truth to show;
Wi' banners rattlin' in the wind,
The Campbells are comin', O-ho, O-ho.

Charlie he's my Darling

'Twas on a Monday morning,
  Right early in the year,
That Charlie came to our town—
  The young Chevalier.

Chorus
An' Charlie, he's my darling,
  My darling, my darling;
Charlie, he's my darling—
  The young Chevalier.

As he was walking up the street,
  The city for to view;
O there he spied a bonnie lass
  The window looking thro'
        An' Charlie, &c

Sae light's he jimped up the stair,
  And tirled at the pin;
And wha sae ready as hersel'
  To let the laddie in?
        An' Charlie, &c

He set his Jenny on his knee,
  All in his Highland dress;
For brawlie weel he ken'd the way
  To please a bonnie lass.
        An' Charlie, &c

It's up yon heathery mountain,
  And down yon scroggy glen,
We daurna gang a-milking
  For Charlie and his men!
        An' Charlie, &c.

Come in, Come in

In the land called Caledonia,
There are certain things you say,
To express your feelings freely,
In the good old Scottish way
"Haste ye back" means call again
   soon,
And "Here's tae us" means good
   cheer,
But these simple words of welcome,
Are the ones I long to hear.

Chorus:
Come in, come in, it's nice to see
   you,
How's yoursel' you're looking grand,
Tak' a seat and ha'e a drammie,
Man you're welcome, here's my
   hand.

So let us gather here this nicht,
And sing of days gone by,
Days of yore that are no longer,
And their passing brings a sigh.
Then with dawn will come the
   parting,
And you'll wander down the glen,
Health be yours and joy be with
   you,
Till you hear those words again.

**Printed and published by kind permission
of James S. Kerr, Music Publishers.**

Comin' through the Rye

Comin' through the rye, poor body,
  Comin' through the rye,
She draigl't a' her petticoatie,
  Comin' through the rye.
    Jenny's a' wat, poor body,
      Jenny's seldom dry;
    She draigl't a' her petticoatie,
      Comin' through the rye.

Gin a body meet a body—
  Comin' through the rye,
Gin a body kiss a body,—
  Need a body cry.
Gin a body meet a body—
  Comin' through the glen,
Gin a body kiss a body,—
  Need the warld ken?
    Jenny's a' wat, poor body,
      Jenny's seldom dry;
    She draigl't a' her petticoatie,
      Comin' through the rye.

Words by Robert Burns

The Cooper o' Fife

There was a wee cooper, who liv'd in Fife,
  Nickety nackety noo, noo, noo,
And he has gotten a gentle wife;
Hey Willie wal-la-chy!
Now John Dougal alane,
  Quo rushety roo roo roo!

She wadna bake, she wadna brew;
  Nickety Nackety noo, noo, noo;
For spoilin' o' her comely hue.
Hey Willie wal-la-chy!
Now John Dougal alane,
  Quo rushety roo roo roo!

She wadna card, she wadna spin,
  Nickety Nackety noo noo noo,
For shamin' o' her gentle kin,
Hey Willie wal-la-chy!
Now John Dougal alane,
  Quo rushety roo roo roo!

The cooper's awa to his wool pack
  Nickety Nackety noo, noo, noo;
He's laid a sheepskin on her back;
Hey Willie wal-la-chy!
Now John Dougal alane,
  Quo rushety roo, roo, roo!

I'll no thrash you, ye're oh gentle kin,
  Nickety nackety noo, noo, noo,
But I will leather my ain sheepskin,
Hey Willie wal-la-chy!
Now John Dougal alane,
  Quo rushety roo, roo, roo;

"Oh I will bake and brew, and spin,
  Nickety nackety noo, noo, noo;
"And think nae mair o' my gentle kin",
Hey willie Wal-la-chy!
Now John Dougal alane,
  Quo rushety roo, roo, roo!

All ye who have gotten a gentle wife,
  Nickety nackety noo, noo, noo;
Keep weel in mind the cooper o' Fife,
Hey Willie wal-la-chy!
Now John Dougal alane,
  Quo rushety roo, roo, roo.

Dancing in Kyle

When the sun has gone down in the dark
   Western islands
Our work is all done for a while,
Then we gather to-gether whatever the weather
   And drive to the dancing in Kyle.
Now there's Mairi and Duncan and Morag and
   Calum
   And Flora and Kenna and Don,
And we're driving from Dornie, Glenelg and
   Killilan
And laughing as we race along.

Then Ruari will sing of the beauties of Islay
And Seumas of Stornoway's Isle,
Then the finest of dancers will show us the
   Lancers
   When we go to the dancing in Kyle.
There's the swirl of the kilt and the skirl of the
   pipes
   And Ken Mason's accordion band,
And it's oh! for the eightsome and ah! for the jig
   And the Dashing White Sergeant is grand.

Soon the dawn will be showing, the great
   mountains glowing,
   And we must drive many a mile,
But we'll leave Inverinate and Ardelve and
   Dornie
   Next time that there's dancing in Kyle.
And we'll arm and we'll swing and we'll heuch
   and we'll sing
   And we'll set to our partners in style,
For there's nothing so grand in the whole of
   the land
   As to go to the dancing in Kyle.

**Printed and published by kind permission
of James S. Kerr, Music Publishers.**

The De'il's awa wi' the Exciseman

The deil cam fiddling thro' the town,
 And danc'd awa' wi' th' Exciseman;
And ilka wife cries, auld Mahoun,
 I wish you luck o' the prize, man.

Chorus
The deil's awa', the deil's awa',
 The deil's awa' wi' th' Exciseman;
He's danc'd awa', he's danc'd awa',
 He's danc'd awa' wi' th' Exciseman.

We'll mak our maut, and we'll brew our drink,
 We'll laugh, sing, and rejoice, man;
And mony braw thanks to the meikle black deil,
 That danc'd awa' wi' th' Exciseman.
            The deil's awa', &c

There's threesome reels, there's foursome reels,
 There's hornpipes and strathspeys, man,
But the ae best dance e'er cam to the land,
 Was the deil's awa' wi' th' Exciseman.
            The deil's awa', &c.

Words by Robert Burns

Donald where's your Troosers?

I've just come down from the
  Isle of Skye,
I'm no' very big and I'm awful
  shy,
And the lassies shout when I go
  by,
"Donald where's your troosers?"

CHORUS:
Let the wind blow high,
Let the wind blow low,
Through the streets in my kilt
  I'll go,
And all the ladies say, "Hello,
Donald, where's your trousers?"

A lassie took me to a ball,
And it was slippery in the hall,
And I was feart that I would fall,
For I hadnae on ma troosers.

I went down to London town,
And I had some fun in the Under-
  ground,
The ladies turn their heads
  around, saying,
"Donald, where are your
  trousers?"

To wear the kilt is my delight,
It isna wrong, I know it's right,
The Islanders would get a fright,
If they saw me in the troosers.

They'd like to wed me everywan,
Just let them catch me if they
   can,
You cannae tak' the breeks aff a
   Heilan' man,
And I don't wear the troosers.

**Printed and published by kind permission
of James S. Kerr, Music Publishers.**

Duncan Gray

Duncan Gray cam' here to woo,
Ha, ha, the woo-in' o't;
On blythe Yule nicht when we were fu',
Ha, ha, the woo-in' o't.
Maggie coost her head fu' high,
Look'd a-sklent, and unco skeigh,
Gart puir Duncan stand abeigh,
Ha, ha, the woo'in o't.

Duncan fleech'd, and Duncan pray'd,
Ha, ha, the wooin' o't;
Meg was deaf as Ailsa Craig,
Ha, ha, the wooin' o't.
Duncan sigh'd baith out an' in,
Grat his een baith blear'd an' blin',
Spak' o' lowpin' o'er a linn,
Ha, ha, the wooin' o't.

Time and chance are but a tide,
Ha, ha, the wooin' o't;
Slighted love is sair to bide,
Ha, ha, the wooin' o't.
Shall, I like a fool, quo' he,
For a haughty hizzie dee?
She may gae to—France—for me!
Ha, ha, the wooin' o't.

How it comes let doctors tell,
Ha, ha, the wooin' o't;
Meg grew sick as he grew hale,
Ha, ha, the wooin' o't.
Something in her bosom wrings,
For relief a sigh she brings,
And, oh! her een, they spak' sic things,
Ha, ha, the wooin' o't.

Duncan was a lad o' grace,
Ha, ha the wooin' o't;
Maggie's was a piteous case,
Ha, ha, the wooin' o't.
Duncan couldna be her death,
Swelling pity smoor'd his wrath;
Now they're crouse and canty baith,
Ha, ha, the wooin' o't.

Words by Robert Burns

Green Grow the Rashes

Green grow the rashes, O;
Green grow the rashes, O;
The sweetest hours that e'er I spend,
  Are spent amang the lasses, O.

There's nought but care on ev'ry han',
  In ev'ry hour that passes, O:
What signifies the life o' man,
  An' 'twere na for the lasses, O.
              Green grow, &c

The warly race may riches chase,
  An' riches still may fly them, O;
An' tho' at last they catch them fast,
  Their hearts can ne'er enjoy them, O.
              Green grow, &c

But gie me a canny hour at e'en,
  My arms about my Dearie, O;
An' warly cares, an' warly men,
  May a' gae tapsalteerie, O!
              Green grow, &c

Words by Robert Burns

Hey Johnnie Cope

Cope sent a challenge frae Dunbar,
"Charlie, meet me an ye daur,
And I'll learn you the art o' war,
If you'll meet wi' me in the morning."

Hey, Johnnie Cope, are ye waukin' yet?
Or are your drums a beatin' yet?
If ye were waukin' I wad wait,
To gang to the coals i' the morning.

When Charlie look'd the letter upon,
He drew his sword the scabbard from;
"Come, follow, me, my merry men,
And we'll meet Johnnie Cope i' the morning."
Hey, Johnnie Cope, &c

Now, Johnnie, be as good as your word,
Come, let us try baith fire and sword.
And dinna flee like a frighted bird
That's chased frae its nest i' the morning.
Hey, Johnnie Cope &c

When Johnnie Cope he heard of this,
He thought it wadna be amiss
To hae a horse in readiness
To flee awa' i' the morning.
Hey, Johnnie Cope &c

Fye, now, Johnnie, get up an' rin,
The Highland bagpipes mak' a din;
It's best to sleep in a hale skin,
For 'twill be a bluidie morning.
Hey, Johnnie Cope &c

When Johnnie Cope to Dunbar came,
They spier'd at him, "Where's a' your men?"
"The deil confounded me gin I ken,
  For I left them a' i' the morning."
                    Hey Johnnie Cope &c

Now, Johnnie, troth, ye were na blate,
To come wi' the news o' your ain defeat,
And leave your men in sic a strait,
  So early in the morning.
                    Hey Johnnie Cope &c

"In faith," quo' Johnnie, "I got sic flegs,
Wi' their claymores and filabegs,
If I face them deil break my legs,
  So I wish you a' a good morning."
                    Hey Johnnie Cope &c.

An old Jacobite song.

from General
J. Cope

Highland Laddie

The bonniest lad that e'er I saw,
  Bonnie laddie, Highland laddie;
Wore a plaid and was fu' braw,
  Bonnie Highland laddie.
On his head a bonnet blue,
  Bonnie laddie, Highland laddie;
His loyal heart was firm and true,
  Bonnie Highland laddie.

Trumpets sound, and cannons roar,
  Bonnie lassie, Lowland lassie;
And a' the hills wi' echoes roar,
  Bonnie Lowland lassie.
Glory, honour, now invite,
  Bonnie lassie, Lowland lassie,
For freedom and my king to fight,
  Bonnie Lowland lassie.

The sun a backward course shall take,
  Bonnie laddie, Highland laddie;
Ere aught thy manly courage shake,
  Bonnie Highland laddie.
Go! for yoursel' procure renown,
  Bonnie laddie, Highland laddie;
And for your lawful king, his crown,
  Bonnie Highland laddie.

Words by Robert Burns

Hiking Song

O the Wanderlust is on
  me
And tonight I strike the trail,
And the morning sun will
  find me
  In the lovely Lomond Vale,
Then I'll hike it thro' Glen
  Falloch,
  Where the mountain breezes blow,
And I'll drum up in the evening
  In the valley of Glencoe.

CHORUS:
Then swing along to a hiking song
  On the highway winding
  west,
Tramping Highland glens
  and bracken bens,
  To greet the Isles we love
  the best
Islay, Jura, Scarba, Lunga
  And the Islands of the Sea,
Luing and Mull, Colonsay,
  Staffa, Coll, Iona and
  Tiree.
  "Sgur" of Eigg and Rhum
  and Canna
With the Minch waves
  rolling high
And the heather-tinted
  Cuillins
  Of the lovely Isle of Skye.

When the Wandering will
    leave me
As I grow too old to roam,
Still the memory will linger
    Of my lovely Highland
    home;
Silv'ry streams and rambling
    rivers,
    Verdant vales and glorious
    glens
And the pride of Caledonia's
    Heather and bracken bens.

**Printed and Published by kind permission of
James S. Kerr, Music Publishers.**

The Hundred Pipers

Wi' a hundred pipers an' a', an' a',
Wi' a hundred pipers an' a', an' a';
We'll up an' gie them a blaw, a blaw,
Wi' a hundred pipers an' a', an' a'.

Oh! it's owre the Border awa', awa',
It's owre the Border awa', awa',
We'll on and we'll march to Carlisle ha',
Wi' its yetts, its castell, an' a', an' a'.

Oh! our sodger lads looked braw, looked braw,
Wi' their tartans, kilts an' a', an' a',
Wi' their bonnets, an' feathers, an' glittering gear,
An' pibrochs sounding sweet and clear.
Will they a' return to their ain dear glen?
Will they a' return, our Hieland men?
Second-sighted Sandy looked fu' wae,
And mothers grat when they marched away.
                    Wi' a hundred pipers, &c

Oh wha is foremost o' a', o' a'?
Oh wha does follow the blaw, the blaw?
Bonnie Charlie, the king o' us a', hurra!
Wi' his hundred pipers an' a', an' a'.
His bonnet an' feather, he's wavin' high,
His prancin' steed maist seems to fly,
The nor' wind plays wi' his curly hair,
While the pipers blaw in an unco flare.
                    Wi' a hundred pipers &c

The Esk was swollen, sae red and sae deep,
But shouther to shouther the brave lads keep;
Twa thousand swam owre to fell English ground,
An' danced themselves dry to the pibroch's sound.

Dumfounder'd the English saw—they saw—
Dumfounder'd, they heard the blaw, the blaw;
Dumfounder'd, they a' ran awa', awa',
From the hundred pipers an' a', an' a'.
      Wi' a hundred pipers an' a', an' a',
      Wi a hundred pipers an' a', an' a',
      We'll up and gie them a blaw, a blaw,
      Wi' a hundred pipers an' a', an' a'.

Words by Lady Nairne

The Laird o' Cockpen

The laird o' Cockpen, he's proud and he's great,
His mind is ta'en up wi' things o' the State;
He wanted a wife, his braw house to keep,
But favour wi' wooin' was fashious to seek.

Down by the dyke-side a lady did dwell,
At his table head he thought she'd look well,
McClish's ae daughter o' Clavers-ha' Lee,
A penniless lass wi' a lang pedigree.

His wig was weel pouther'd and as gude as new,
His waistcoat was white, his coat it was blue;
He put on a ring, a sword and cock'd hat,
And wha could refuse the laird wi' a' that?

He took the grey mare, and rade cannily,
An' rapp'd at the yett o' Clavers-ha' Lee;
"Gae tell Mistress Jean to come speedily ben,—
She's wanted to speak to the Laird o' Cockpen."

Mistress Jean was makin' the elder-flower wine;
"An' what brings the laird at sic a like time?"
She put aff her apron, and on her silk gown,
Her mutch wi' red ribbons, and gaed awa' down.

An' when she cam' ben he bowed fu' low,
An' what was his errand he soon let her know;
Amazed was the laird when the lady said "Na",
And wi' a laigh curtsie she turned awa'.

Dumfounder'd was he, nae sigh did he gie,
He mounted his mare—he rade cannily;
An' aften he thought, as he gaed through the glen,
She's daft to refuse the laird o' Cockpen.

And now that the laird his exit had made,
Mistress Jean she reflected on what she had said;
"Oh, for ane I'll get better, its waur I'll get ten,
I was daft to refuse the Laird o' Cockpen."

Next time that the laird and the lady were seen,
They were gaun arm-in-arm to the kirk on the green;
Now she sits in the ha' like a weel-tappit hen,
But as yet there's nae chickens appear'd at Cockpen.

Words by Lady Nairne

Linten Lowrin

I sheared my first hairst in Bogend,
Doun by the fit o' Benachie;
And sair I wrought and sair I fought,
But I wan out my penny fee.
    Linten lowrin, lowrin linten,
    Linten lowrin, linten lee;
    I'll gang the gait I cam' again,
    And a better bairnie I will be.

O! Rhynie's wark is ill to work,
And Rhynie's wages are but sma';
And Rhynie's laws are double straight,
And that does grieve me maist of a'.
    Linten lowrin, &c.

O! Rhynie is a Hieland place,
It doesna suit a Lawland loon;
And Rhynie is a cauld clay hole,
It is na like my faither's toun.
    Linten lowrin, &c.

Old Aberdeenshire Song.

My ain Folk

Far frae my hame I
   wander;
But still my thoughts return
To my ain folk ower yonder,
In the sheiling by the burn.
I see the cosy ingle,
   And the mist abune the brae:
And joy and sadness mingle,
As I list some auld-warld lay.

CHORUS:
And it's oh! but I'm longing
   for my ain folk,
Tho' they be but lowly, puir,
   and plain folk:
I am far beyond the sea,
But my heart will ever be
At hame in dear auld Scotland
   Wi' my ain folk!

O' their absent ane they're
   telling
   The auld folk by the fire:
And I mark the swift tears
   welling,
As the ruddy flame leaps high'r.
How the mither wad caress me
   Were I but by her side:
Now she prays that heav'n
   will bless me
Though the stormy seas divide.

A bonnie lass is greeting,
Tho' she strives to stay the tears;
Ah! sweet will be our meeting
After mony weary years.
Soon my fond arms shall enfold ye,
    As I ca' you ever mine.
Still abides the love I told ye
In the days of auld lang syne.

And it's oh! but I'm longing
    for my ain folk,
Tho' they be but lowly, puir,
    and plain folk:
I am far beyond the sea,
But soon again I'll be
At hame in dear auld Scotland
    Wi' my ain folk!

Words by Wilfred Mills. Reprinted by permission of the copyright owners, Messrs. Boosey and Hawkes, London, Music Publishers Ltd.

My Heart's in the Highlands

My heart's in the Highlands, my heart is not here,
My heart's in the Highlands a-chasing the deer—
A-chasing the wild deer, and following the roe:
My heart's in the Highlands, wherever I go.

Farewell to the Highlands, farewell to the North—
The birth place of Valour, the country of Worth:
Wherever I wander, wherever I rove,
The hills of the Highlands for ever I love.

Farewell to the mountains high cover'd with snow;
Farewell to the straths and green valleys below;
Farewell to the forests and wild-hanging woods;
Farewell to the torrents and loud-pouring floods.

My heart's in the Highlands, my heart is not here,
My heart's in the Highlands a-chasing the deer—
Chasing the wild deer, and following the roe:
My heart's in the Highlands, wherever I go.

Words by Robert Burns

My Love she's but a Lassie yet

My love she's but a lassie yet,
  My love she's but a lassie yet;
We'll let her stand a year or twa,
  She'll no be half sae saucy yet.

I rue the day I saw her, O,
  I rue the day I saw her, O;
Wha gets her needs na say she's woo'd,
  But he may say he's bought her, O!

Come, draw a drap o' the best o't yet,
  Come, draw a drap o' the best o't yet;
Gae seek for pleasure where ye will,
  But here I never miss'd it yet,
We're a' dry wi' drinking o't,
    We're a' dry wi' drinking o't;
The minister kiss'd the fiddler's wife,
  And couldna preach for thinkin' o't.

Words by Robert Burns

Northern Lights of old Aberdeen

When I was a lad, a tiny wee lad,
    My mother said to me,
"Come see the Northern lights, my boy,
They're bright as they can be."
She called them the heavenly dancers,
    Merry dancers in the sky;
I'll never forget that wonderful sight, they made
    the heavens bright.

CHORUS:
The Northern Lights of Old Aberdeen
Mean Home Sweet Home to me,
The Northern Lights of Aberdeen are what I long
    to see.
I've been a wand'rer all of my life and many a
    sight I've seen,
God speed the day when I'm on my way
To my home in Aberdeen.

I've wandered in many far-off lands, and travelled
    many a mile.
I've missed the folk I've cherished most, the joy
    of a friendly smile.
It warms up the heart of the wand'rer, the clasp
    of a welcoming hand
To greet me when I return, home to my native
    land.

**Printed and published by kind permission
of James S. Kerr, Music Publishers.**

A Red, Red Rose

O my luve's like a red, red rose
  That's newly sprung in June.
O my Luve's like the melodie
  That's sweetly play'd in tune.

As fair art thou, my bonnie lass,
  So deep in luve am I;
And I will love thee still, my Dear,
  Till a' the seas gang dry.

Till a' the seas gang dry, my Dear,
  And the rocks melt wi' the sun:
I will love thee still, my Dear,
  While the sand o' life shall run:

And fare thee weel, my only Luve:
  And fare thee weel, a while!
And I will come again, my Luve,
  Tho' it were ten thousand mile!

Words by Robert Burns

The Rigs o' Barley

It was upon a Lammas night,
    When corn rigs are bonnie,
Beneath the moon's unclouded light,
    I held away to Annie;
The time flew by wi' tentless heed,
    Till 'tween the late and early,
Wi' sma' persuasion, she agreed
    To see me thro' the barley.

The sky was blue, the wind was still,
    The moon was shining clearly:
I set her down, wi' right good will,
    Amang the rigs o' barley:
I ken't her heart was a' my ain:
    I lov'd her most sincerely;
I kiss'd her owre and owre again,
    Amang the rigs o' barley.

I lock'd her in my fond embrace!
    Her heart was beating rarely:
My blessings on that happy place,
    Amang the rigs o' barley!
But by the moon and stars so bright,
    That shone that hour so clearly!
She aye shall bless that happy night,
    Amang the rigs o' barley.

I ha'e been blithe wi' comrades dear;
I ha'e been merry drinking;
I ha'e been joyfu' gatherin' gear;
    I ha'e been happy thinkin':
But a' the pleasures e'er I saw,
    Tho' three times doubled fairly,
That happy night was worth them a',
    Amang the rigs o' barley.

CHORUS:
Corn rigs, an' barley rigs,
  An' corn rigs are bonnie:
I'll ne'er forget that happy night,
  Amang the rigs wi' Annie.

Words by Robert Burns

Road to Dundee

Cauld winter was howlin' o'er muir and o'er
  mountains,
And wild was the surge on the dark rolling
  sea;
When I met about daybreak a bonnie young
  lassie,
Wha' asked me the road and the miles to
  Dundee.

Says I, "My young lassie, I canna' weel tell ye,
  The road and the distance I canna' weel gi'e,
But if you'll permit me tae gang a wee bittie,
  I'll show you the road and the miles to
  Dundee."

At once she consented, and gave me her arm,
  Ne'er a word did I speir wha' the lassie might
  be;
She appeared like an angel in feature and form,
  As she walked by my side on the road to Dundee.

At length wi' the Howe o' Strathmartine behind
  us,
And the spires o' the toon in full view we
  could see;
She said, "Gentle sir, I can never forget ye,
  For showing me so far on the road to
  Dundee."

I took the gowd pin from the scarf on my
  bosom,
And said, "Keep ye this in remembrance o'
  me."
Then bravely I kissed the sweet lips o' the lassie,
  Ere I parted wi' her on the road to Dundee.

So here's to the lassie—I ne'er can forget her—
  And ilka young laddie that's listening to me;
And never be sweer to convoy a young lassie,
  Though it's only to show her the road to
  Dundee.

**Printed and Published by kind permission
of James S. Kerr, Music Publishers.**

Road to the Isles

It's a far croonin' that is pullin' me away
As take I wi' my cromak to the road,
The far Coolins are puttin' love on me
As step I wi' the sunlight for my load.

Sure by Tummel and Loch Rannoch and Lochaber
   I will go,
By heather tracks wi' heaven in their wiles;
If it's thinkin' in your inner heart
   braggart's in my step,
You've never smelt the tangle o' the Isles,
Oh, the far Coolins are puttin' love on me,
As step I wi' my cromak to the Isles.

It's by Sheil water the track is to the west,
By Aillort and by Morar to the sea,
The cool cresses I am thinkin' o' for pluck,
And bracken for a wink on Mother knee.
Sure, by &c.

It's the blue islands are pullin' me away,
Their laughter puts the leap up on the lame,
The blue islands from the Skerries to the Lews,
Wi' heather honey taste upon each name.
Sure, by &c.

Printed and published by kind permission of the copyright holders Messrs. Boosey and Hawkes, Music Publishers, London.

Printed and published by permission of the Trustees of the Estate of Marjory Kennedy-Fraser and Boosey and Hawkes Music Publishers Ltd.

Rowan Tree

Oh, rowan tree! Oh, rowan tree! Thou'lt aye be dear tae me,
Entwined thou art wi' mony ties o' hame and infancy;
Thy leaves were aye the first o' spring, thy flow'rs the
summer's pride,
There wasnae sic a bonny tree in a' the countryside.
Oh, rowan tree!

How fair wert thou in summer time, wi' a' thy clusters white,
How rich and gay thy autumn dress, wi' berries red and
bright,
We sat aneath thy spreading shade, the bairnies round thee
ran,
They pu'd thy bonnie berries red and necklaces they strang.
Oh, rowan tree!

On thy fair stem were mony names, which now nae mair I
see.
But they're engraven on my heart, forgot they ne'er can be!
My mother! Oh! I see her still, she smil'd our sports to see,
Wi' little Jeannie on her lap, wi' Jamie at her knee!
Oh, rowan tree!

Oh, there arose my father's prayer, in holy evening's calm,
How sweet was then my mother's voice, in the Martyr's
psalm.
Now a' are gane! We meet nae mair aneath the rowan tree,
But hallowed thoughts around thee twine o' hame and infancy.
Oh, rowan tree!

**Printed and published by kind permission
of James S. Kerr, Music Publishers.**

Scotland the Brave

Hark when the night is falling,
Hear, hear the pipes are calling,
Loudly and proudly calling
Down through the glen.
There where the hills are sleeping,
Now feel the blood a-leaping,
High as the spirits of the old Highland men.

Towering in gallant fame,
Scotland, my mountain hame
High may your proud standards gloriously wave.
Land of the high endeavour,
Land of the shining river,
Land of my heart for ever,
Scotland the Brave.

High in the misty Highlands,
Out by the purple islands,
Brave are the hearts that beat
Beneath Scottish skies.
Wild are the winds to meet you,
Staunch are the friends that
    greet you,
Kind as the love that shines
From fair maidens' eyes.

[Author not known].

A Scottish Soldier

There was a soldier, a Scottish soldier,
Who wandered far away and soldiered far away;
There was none bolder, with good broad shoulder,
He's fought in many a fray,
And fought and won!
He'd seen the glory and told the story
Of battles glorious
And deeds victorious,
But now he's sighing, his heart is crying,
To leave these green hills of Tyrol.

CHORUS:
Because these green hills are not Highland hills,
Or the island hills they're not my land's hills!
And fair as these green foreign hills may be,
They are not the hills of home.

And now this soldier, this Scottish soldier,
Who'd wandered far away and soldiered far away,
Sees leaves are falling and death is calling,
And he will fade away in that far land!
He called his piper, his trusty piper,
And bade him sound a lay,
A pibroch sad to play,
Upon a hillside, but Scottish hillside,
Not on these green hills of Tyrol.

And so this soldier, this Scottish soldier,
Will wander far no more and soldier far no more,
And on a hillside, a Scottish hillside,
You'll see a piper play
His soldier home!
He'd seen the glory, he'd told his story
Of battles glorious
And deeds victorious;
The bugles cease now, he is at peace now,
Far from those green hills of Tyrol.

**Printed and published by kind permission
of James S. Kerr, Music Publishers.**

Scots, wha hae wi' Wallace Bled

Scots, wha hae wi' Wallace bled!
Scots, wham Bruce has often led,
Welcome to your gory bed,
Or to victory!
Now's the day, and now's the hour;
See the front o' battle lour;
See approach proud Edward's power,
Chains and slavery!

Wha will be a traitor knave?
Wha can fill a coward's grave?
Wha sae base as be a slave
   Let him turn and flee.
Wha for Scotland's king and law,
Freedom's sword will strongly draw,
Freeman stand, or freeman fa',
   Let him follow me!

By oppression's woes and pains,
By your sons in servile chains,
We will drain our dearest veins,
   But they shall be free.
Lay the proud usurpers low!
Tyrants fall in every foe!
Liberty's in every blow!
   Let us do or die!

Words by Robert Burns

Skye Boat Song

Speed, bonnie boat, like a bird on the wing,
  Onward, the sailors cry,
  Carry the lad that's born to be king
Over the sea to Skye.
  Loud the winds howl, loud the waves roar,
  Thunder-clouds rend the air;
  Baffled, our foes stand by the shore;
  Follow, they will not dare.
      Speed, bonnie boat, &c.

Though the waves leap, soft shall ye sleep:
Ocean's a royal bed;
Rocked in the deep, Flora will keep
Watch by your weary head.
      Speed, bonnie boat, &c.

Many's the lad fought on that day
Well the claymore could wield,
When the night came silently lay
Dead on Culloden's field.
      Speed, bonnie boat, &c.

Burned are our homes, exile and death
Scatter the loyal men,
Yet ere the sword cool in the sheath
Charlie will come again.
      Speed, bonnie boat, &c.

Harold Boulton
Printed and published by kind permission
J.B. Cramer & Co. Ltd., London.

Song of the Clyde

I sing of a river I'm happy beside,
The song that I sing is a song of the Clyde.
Of all Scottish rivers it's dearest to me,
It flows from Leadhills all the way to the sea.

It borders the orchards of Lanark so fair;
Meanders through meadows with sheep grazing there:
But from Glasgow to Greenock, in towns on each side
The hammers' "Ding-dong" is the song of the Clyde.

CHORUS:
Oh the river Clyde the wonderful Clyde!
The name of it thrills me and fills me with pride,
And I'm satisfied, what e'er may be-tide,
The sweetest of songs is the Song of the Clyde.

Imagine we've left Craigendoran behind,
And wind happy yachts by Kilcreggan we find;
At Kirn and Dunoon and Innellan we stay;
Then Scotland's Madeira that's Rothesay, they say.
Or maybe by Fairlie or Largs we will go;
Or over to Millport that thrills people so;
Maybe journey to Arran it can't be denied,
Those scenes all belong to the Song of the Clyde.

When sun sets on dockland,
There's beauty to see.
The cry of a sea-bird is music to me,
The blast of a horn loudly echoes, and then,
A stillness descends on the water again.
'Tis here that the sea-going liners are born,
But, unlike the salmon, they seldom return,
Can you wonder the Scots o'er the ocean so wide,
Should constantly long for the Song of the Clyde.

Optional Patter verse

There's Paw an' Maw at Glasgow Broomielaw;
They're goin' "doon the water" for "The Fair."
There's Bob an' Mary on the Govan Ferry,
Wishin' jet propulsion could be there.
There's steamers cruisin', and there's 'buddies' snoozin';
And there's laddies fishin' frae the pier;
An' Paw's perspirin', very near expirin',
As he rows a boat frae there to here.
With eyes a-flashin', it is voted "smashin'",
To be walkin' daily on the Prom:
And May and Evelyn are in seventh heaven
As they stroll along with Dick and Tom.
And Dumbarton Rock to ev'ry Jean and Jock,
Extends a welcome that is high and wide:
Seems to know that they are on their homeward way
To hear the Song of the Clyde.

**Printed and Published by kind permission
of James S Kerr Music Publishers.**

Sound the Pibroch

Sound the pibroch loud on high
  Frae John o' Groats to isle o' Skye,
  Let a' the clans their slogan cry,
And rise and follow Charlie.
      Tha tighin fodham, fodham, fodham,
      Tha tighin fodham, fodham, fodham,
      Tha tighin fodham, fodham, fodham,
      Tha tighin fodham, eirigh!

And see a small devoted band
By dark Loch Shiel have ta'en their stand,
And proudly vow with heart and hand
To fight for royal Charlie.
      Tha tighin fodham, &c.

From every hill and every glen
Are gathering fast the loyal men,
They grasp their dirks and shout again
"Hurrah! for royal Charlie!"
      Tha tighin fodham, &c.

On dark Culloden's field of gore
Hark! Hark! they shout "Claymore! Claymore!"
They bravely fight, what can they more?
They die for royal Charlie.
      Tha tighin fodham, &c.

No more we'll see such deeds again,
Deserted is each Highland glen,
And lonely cairns are o'er the men
Who fought and died for Charlie.
      Tha tighin fodham, &c.

Mrs Norman Macleod [Senior].
Printed and published by kind permission
of J. B. Cramer & Co. Ltd., London.

The Twa Corbies

As I was walking a' alane,
I heard twa corbies making their mane;
The tane unto the tither did say
"Whar sall we gang and dine the day?"

"In behint yon auld fail dyke
I wot there lies a new-slain knight;
And naebody kens that he lies there
But his hawk and his hound and his lady fair."

"His hound is to the huntin' gane
His hawk to fetch the wild-fowl hame,
His lady's taen anither mate,
Sae we may mak' our dinner sweet."

"Ye'll sit on his white hause-bane,
And I'll pike out his bonnie blue e'en;
Wi' ae lock o' his gowden hair
We'll theek our nest whar it grows bare."

"Mony's the ane for him mak's mane,
But nane sall ken whar he is gane;
Owre his white banes, when they are bare,
The wind sall blaw for evermair."

Words by Robert Burns

Weaving Song

Gae owre the muir, gae doun the brae,
Gae busk my bower to mak' it ready,
For I'm gaun' there to wed the day
The bonnie lad that wears the plaidie.

> Twine weel the bonnie tweel,
> Twist weel the plaidie,
> For O! I lo'e the laddie weel
> That wears the tartan plaidie.

Content his lowly cot I'll share,
I ask nae mair to mak' life cheerie;
Wi' heart sae leal and love sae true
The langest day can ne'er seem eerie.
> Twine weel, &c.

Weel sheltered in his Hieland plaid
Frae worldly cares I'll aye be easy;
Its storms I'll hear like blasts that blaw
Owre heather bell and mountain daisy.
> Twine weel, &c.

We're no awa to Bide awa

CHORUS:
For we're no awa' to bide awa'
  We're no' awa' to leave ye
We're no' awa' to bide awa'
  We'll aye come back and see
  ye.

As I gaed doon by Wilsontoon
  I met auld Johnnie Scobbie,
Says I to him will ye hae a hauf,
  Says he, "Man! That's my
  hobby."

So we had a hauf an' anither
  hauf,
And then we had anither,
When he got fou' he shouted
  "Hoo!
  It's Carnwath Mill for ever."

We wandered doon the street
  again
We cleekit unco cheery,
When John got hame his wife
  cried shame,
I see you're enjoyin' your
  hobby.

Of a' the friens that ere I kenned,
  There's nane like Johnnie
  Scobbie,
His hert is leal, he's true as
  steel,
An' a hauf is aye his hobby.

So whenever friendly friens may
   meet,
Wherever Scots foregather,
We'll raise our gless, we'll shout
   Hurroo,
It's Carnwath Mill for ever.

**Printed and published by kind permission
of James S. Kerr, Music Publishers.**

Will Ye No Come Back Again

Bonnie Charlie's now awa',
    Safely owre the friendly main;
Mony a heart will break in twa,
    Should he ne'er come back again.

Will ye no come back again?
Will ye no come back again?
Better lo'ed ye canna be,
Will ye no come back again?

Ye trusted in your Hieland men,
    They trusted you, dear Charlie;
They kent you hiding in the glen,
    Your cleadin' was but barley.
                    Will ye no &c.

English bribes were a' in vain,
    An e'en tho' puirer we may be;
Siller canna buy the heart
    That beats aye for thine and thee.
                    Will ye no &c.

We watched thee in the gloamin' hour,
    We watched thee in the mornin' grey;
Tho' thirty thousand pounds they'd gi'e,
    Oh there was nane that wad betray.
                    Will ye no &c.

Sweet's the laverock's note and lang,
    Lilting wildly up the glen;
But aye to me he sings ae sang,—
    Will ye no come back again?
                    Will ye no &c.

Words by Lady Nairn

Ye Jacobites by Name

Ye Jacobites by name, give an ear, give an ear;
Ye Jacobites by name, give an ear;
Ye Jacobites by name,
Your fautes I will proclaim,
Your doctrines I maun blame—
   You shall hear.

What is right and what is wrang, by the law, by the law?
What is right and what is wrang, by the law?
What is right and what is wrang?
A short sword and a lang,
A weak arm, and a strang,
   For to draw.

What makes heroic strife, fam'd afar, fam'd afar?
What makes heroic strife, fam'd afar?
What makes heroic strife?
To whet th' assassin's knife,
Or hunt a parent's life
   Wi' bluidie war.

Then let your schemes alone, in the state, in the state;
Then let your schemes alone, in the state;
Then let your schemes alone,
Adore the rising sun,
And leave a man undone
   To his fate.